The
HEREFORDS[
and
WORCESTERSHIRE
WEATHER
BOOK

The HEREFORDSHIRE *and* WORCESTERSHIRE WEATHER BOOK

Paul Damari

COUNTRYSIDE BOOKS
NEWBURY, BERKSHIRE

First Published 1995
© Paul Damari 1995

All rights reserved. No reproduction
permitted without the prior permission
of the publishers:

COUNTRYSIDE BOOKS
3 Catherine Road
Newbury, Berkshire

ISBN 1 85306 291 X

Front Cover: A gallant policeman comes to the rescue near the
Belmont Road roundabout, Hereford, on 10th December, 1965.

Back Cover: The result of seven hours of snowfall on
8th February, 1985.

Designed by Mon Mohan

Produced through MRM Associates Ltd., Reading
Typeset by Paragon Typesetters, Queensferry, Clwyd
Printed by Woolnough Bookbinding, Irthlingborough

FOREWORD

I was born on 18th January 1951 in Worcester, and it has always been a standing joke in the family that I gained my interest in the weather from an unusual phenomenon which took place months before my birth. A violent thunderstorm broke over the city, and a bolt of lightning struck my parents' home, causing much damage.

I remember clearly as a boy the hours spent sitting in the window watching the ever-changing weather, fascinated by the varying landscapes and the hues which constantly enhanced the skyline. At that time it became apparent to me why songwriters, poets and such famous composers as Elgar were inspired by weather and landscape.

It was not long before I put together a variety of weather-related books and papers which would come to contain accurate and detailed information on past weather events such as the Frost Fairs of the Little Ice Age in the 1800s, the cold winters of 1946/7 and 1962/3 and the outstanding summers of 1911, 1959, 1975 and 1976.

During my schooldays my interest in the weather gained momentum and come rain or shine I would visit the thermometer screen to take daily readings. For around 19 years I worked for the Worcester Parks Department, and during studies at the Pershore Horticultural College came into contact with their own weather station, which passed results to the Meteorological Office. This further inspired me and it was at this time I realised how fascinating the climate of Herefordshire and Worcestershire was, and how it differed from one county to the next. I began issuing forecasts and observations of my own through the local media, and set up my own weather station. I was elected a Fellow

of the Royal Meteorological Society in 1975. That was the year, of course, before the famous drought, which finally ended on the Bank Holiday as torrential cloudbursts of monsoon intensity lashed the county for three months, creating the wettest autumn on record.

While providing weather data and forecasts for the *Worcester Evening News* and *Berrows Newspaper*, the business snowballed. Radio Wyvern came on the scene, followed later by BBC Hereford and Worcester. More than ten years ago I set up my own company, Weather Communications, with my wife Sandra and we now have hundreds of weather-related clients from all over the UK. Our station is also an official Climatological Station for the Meteorological Office, sending in monthly observations.

The combination of outstanding countryside and ever-changing weather, from wonderful sunsets to bitter cold and sun-kissed landscapes, most definitely shaped my career. This book is all about that weather, and what we have experienced of it in Herefordshire and Worcestershire. This unique record of weather extremes down the years, from heat and drought to storm and tempest, is the result of close collaboration with local historians, newspapers and the general public. I have also drawn in both depth and detail from my own records which now span 25 years.

So join me as we meander through centuries of climatic mayhem – but remember I am cataloguing only the worst weather events. Every cloud has a silver lining and Herefordshire and Worcestershire have a generally pleasant and temperate climate, complementing the picturesque countryside which is both admired by visitors and treasured by all those who live here.

Paul Damari FRMetS
August 1995

A *lightning discharge photographed during the very dry summer of 1976. This produced a natural firework display without rain, as the precipitation evaporated before it reached the ground, due to the very dry surface air.*

CONTENTS

A pint of the hard stuff!

INTRODUCTION

Weathering the Storm

The British are renowned throughout the world for their obsession with the weather. If all else fails while standing at the bus stop, or on meeting friends in the street or at the shops, we will usually find ourselves talking about the Great British Weather. With the Atlantic Ocean out to the west of our island and a large continent to the east, weather forecasting in Britain can be a very tricky occupation. We all know that we can often experience several different types of weather in one day.

Hereford and Worcester are both cathedral cities overflowing with history. However, they lie in very different and contrasting countryside. The weather can, and does, vary greatly from one side of the Malvern Hill range to the other. Although the climate is in general mild and stable, over the centuries the countryside has often been blasted by storm and tempest. The landscape in places shows signs of weathering from long ago, and today the battle against the elements continues.

The rivers Severn and Wye frequently spill over during the late autumn, winter and early spring, flooding adjacent meadows and plains for several days at a time and eroding their banks in places.

On certain occasions through history, various oddities have fallen from the skies over the countryside – from red worms, frogs and fish, to dust and even periwinkles! This weather phenomenon is brought about by violent up-draughts within the large thunder clouds we call cumulonimbus which hoover up these foreign bodies and transport them many miles from their original source, depositing them on the ground within the down-draught of the storm clouds.

Winds of hurricane ferocity have visited the area on numerous occasions, often disastrous for the harvest and the hopfields of the past. Blizzards have frequently blocked roads, and late spring snowfalls have in some years covered the April daffodils with a thick white blanket. Hailstones measuring three quarters of an inch in diameter have stripped foliage from vegetation and played havoc with glasshouses.

Such climatic events have been a part of local life for centuries but, as always, the folk of Herefordshire and Worcestershire have picked themselves up and weathered the storm.

THE WEATHER
IN THE EARLY YEARS

The 12th Century: Famine and Flood

1105: The year ended as it began, with extremely adverse weather conditions throughout. Thunderous rains in January brought freak floods, and late frosts devastated the fruit harvest as the May night temperature plummeted. Summer storms lashed the area day after day with turbulent squalls gusting to damaging force on occasion. Early snows arrived in October, lasting well into November with severe, damaging frosts.

1110: Sudden bitter cold from the east visited the area with devastating effect. The cold lasted the whole spring, with frequent severe frosts which caused much damage to crops, and fruit trees perished over a wide area.

1111: Without warning the area was exposed to an extremely severe winter, which began in November and lasted through to March. Driving snow blocked lanes and roads to a depth of 8 ft. Famine occurred within the animal kingdom, with hundreds of sheep and cattle perishing.

1125: A long cold, wet winter settled across the land, with lashing rain and heavy snowfalls. Such was the ferocity of the winds that widespread damage was reported. Persistent heavy rain combined with melting snow to bring flooding. Disease amongst both animals and humans was rife.

1126: Following that dismal winter, drought struck, bringing famine and the deaths of hundreds of small animals and birds. The air temperature was so high the ground cracked open by as much as 3 ft in midsummer. Water became undrinkable in parts of Herefordshire and Worcestershire for a time and the farming community saw crop after crop fail.

1137: Torrential rain began in late January and it continued wet until Christmas. Flooding was commonplace from streams and rivers alike, and landslides took place. Strong, cold winds ruined the corn crop. Due to the very wet conditions throughout the year numerous types of fungi sprouted and many people were affected by poisoning from eating toadstools.

1178: Winter snows blanketed the landscape with drifts reported up to 12 ft deep. North winds caused much hardship from the cold and there was a lack of food. Snow blanketed the area through the winter months.

1190: Periods of wet prevailed through the year with much disease amongst animals and birds. Flooding was frequent as time after time rain fell on the area. The crops failed very early on, with the harvest ruined.

1196: Famine again visited the area with sudden heavy rains setting everything awash, followed by long periods of drought and heat. Crops were affected by scorch and drought. Drying winds swirled across the countryside, with many grassland fires reported.

Flood level marking plaques from several centuries on Worcester cathedral wall.

The 13th Century: Frost and Drought

1200: Severe cold set in during the autumn with the first snows falling in mid December and lasting through January and February into early March. Lanes became blocked with deep, crisp and hard-packed snow. Waterfalls and streams froze everywhere and with strong polar winds blowing, many people died of frostbite. Thousands of birds were found weak or dead

15

on top of the snow. With the onset of the big thaw in March, spring floods covered large areas of farmland.

1210: An extraordinary frost set in which lasted from New Year's Eve through to St Valentine's Day. Such was its intensity that all our rivers froze over to a great depth. Sales were organised on the rivers and men rode on horseback from Claines in Worcester to Gloucester, while on the rock-solid river Wye people gathered at the weekends to enjoy the pig roasts.

1236: Incessant and torrential rain swept into the area, causing much flooding and hardship to local people. Monsoon-like rains poured from leaden skies through January, February and the first part of March. Livestock was lost and disease spread rapidly amongst animals. During the rest of March dry weather set in and between April and August Herefordshire and Worcestershire basked in hot sunshine. A prolonged drought began, and even after the wet winter water soon became scarce and rivers fell to low levels, especially the Teme and Avon.

1246: After a dry period in March followed by a showery April with cold winds, a sudden severe frost arose, nipping the early spring growth. Much of the fruit blossom in the vales was damaged by the late frost.

1247: Such foul weather set in during the spring that it turned into a second winter. A violent whirlwind was reported to have picked up fowl pens on a Herefordshire farm and deposited them a mile away, stripping the hens of their feathers in the process. Late snowstorms caught out the shepherds of Herefordshire, with snows 15 ft deep. Sudden thaws brought flooding and cold wintry winds created skating rink conditions where flood water lay.

1252: From April to July a severe drought swept the land and caused many of the crops to fail. Water became so scarce that people were reported to be moving out of this area to find water, and transporting it back by horse and cart.

1253: The extreme drought conditions continued through the spring and summer with streams and ponds drying out and rivers running at their lowest levels ever. Hot sun baked the ground rock hard and livestock suffered severely. The autumn suddenly turned wet, with flooding as torrential rain and thunderstorms arrived over the area. Flash flooding was commonplace as Mother Nature balanced her books.

1255: A great drought again struck the land, with little rain and very strong, thirsty winds which again ruined crops, dried out streams and reduced rivers to very low levels. The air was filled with dry dust from late morning to evening during mid summer as high winds whipped up the drought-stricken soil. A dust devil was spotted crossing the countryside north of Ludlow, lifting a column of dry earth more than 200 metres high, snapping off branches from trees and taking with it numerous chicken pens from a nearby farm.

1258: Torrential rain visited the countryside, with winds of such ferocity that many areas were devastated. The river Severn burst its banks during June, with much farmland flooded at harvest time.

1287: A series of good harvests brought the price of wheat down to a figure lower than at any time between 1260 and 1400. Weather conditions were very favourable with equal amounts of rain and sunshine.

The 14th Century: Want and Distress

1305: A drought affected the whole of Herefordshire and Worcestershire, accompanied by such burning heat that cattle died from lack of water. The winter turned bitterly cold with frosts and strong blizzards from 15th December to 25th January. High winds whipped up snow drifts 20 ft deep in country areas, with another intensely cold spell from 13th February to 13th April.

1308-1330: This period stands out in history for the generally very high price of wheat, caused by a succession of wet or indifferent seasons and bad harvests. Incessant rains and cold winters and stormy summers caused havoc within the farming community, forced to watch crops fail and cattle perish from disease and want.

1343-1345: Widespread and frequent droughts accompanied summer heatwaves and strong thirsty winds. Corn was unusually scarce, streams dried out and rivers were at very low levels with cracks up to 5 inches wide in their beds by August 1344.

1351-1370: A time of considerable scarcity. Had the population not been so decimated by the Black Death in 1349, distress in the area would have been as great as during the period 1310 to 1321.

1361-1362: Droughts through the whole of 1361 saw crops fail in Herefordshire and Worcestershire and famine in the area. On 8th January 1362 a tempest of wind levelled high houses, towers and belfries and trees.

The 15th Century: The Great Water

1483: A year noted for its continual monsoon-like rains. The river Wye in Herefordshire and the Severn in Worcestershire rose rapidly, with several people drowning in their beds as the water swept in. The waters did not abate for ten days and the occurrence became commonly known as 'The Great Water'.

The 16th Century: Feast and Famine

1509: With most favourable weather conditions throughout the year, and an equal balance of sunshine and rain, the harvest was abundant, with wheat at its lowest price for two centuries.

1527: A famine year, with great rains and sudden floods during the previous autumn and in the spring at sowing time. Rain of particular intensity fell from 15th April to 3rd June.

1538-1541: Extremely dry years with rainfall almost non-existent and rivers and streams drying out in parts. A remarkable series of droughts, with a burning sun during the summer.

1564: Winter began early this year, with great frosts and early snows in November. Freezing rain hung so heavy on the trees that they broke under the weight. Weather vanes on county churches froze solid, and people had great difficulty getting about due to the deep snow. Rivers froze over, with some people taking advantage of the weather and playing football and bowls on the ice.

THE
SEVENTEENTH CENTURY

Storm and Snow

1603-1605: A very damp and dismal time, with the plague raging and both people and animals suffering great hardship and disease, with a shortage of food supplies and fresh water. Rains were frequent and torrential, broken by periods of drought and extreme heat. The winters were hard with snows deep across Herefordshire and Worcestershire. Altogether a time of great famine and a dearth of wheat and corn.

1607-1608: Such cold prevailed, especially between 5th December and 14th February, that all the streams and rivers in the area froze to such a depth that fires could be lit on the frozen water. County mills were stopped on account of frozen mill streams. Blizzards raged at times through the winter, covering over roads and lanes, and drifts of 25 ft were recorded.

1615: On 16th January began the greatest snows within living memory. Travellers on foot and on horseback were able to walk over the tops of gates, walls and hedges. The snow increased daily until 12th March and there were further snows in April and drifts in the hills until late May. This was followed by a drought with intense heat before violent storms brought flood chaos in August.

1620: Frost Fairs took place on the Thames and to some extent also on the Wye and the Severn, with pig roasts on the two rivers and fires lit as far south as Gloucester. Heavy snows and thick river ice had arrived by 29th November. The Severn flood followed the severe winter weather. At Homestone's Loade (Hampton Lode) 68 people were drowned as they were going to Bewdley fair.

1622: January and the preceding months were like summer, but on 18th February at about 4 am a high and tempestuous wind brought lightning and storms. Barns, steeples, chimneys and other high edifices were blown down, and many great trees were felled, especially the elms. Continued rain over the next two months made April late for seed sowing, with spring grass early owing to the generally mild temperatures. December saw the return of the great frosts, with the Wye and the Severn freezing over.

1640: An extremely backward spring for grass and fruit, especially in Herefordshire, with weather conditions continuously changing. On 3rd, 4th and 5th July fearsome thunder and lightning ushered in a great flood and many corn fields were damaged, with houses struck by lightning. From 5th to 21st September there was such heavy rainfall that the harvests were ruined.

1683-1684: A cold winter brought the longest frost on record, when elm, oak, ash and walnut trees died from the intense cold. Ice on the rivers was 11 inches thick. Booths and tents were erected for selling wares, especially on the Wye near Hereford and Hay-on-Wye. A severe drought followed in the summer, with very high temperatures.

1698: A cold and wet season. On 8th May an extraordinary spell of frost and snow moved into the area and many parts of Herefordshire were cut off for a while. The cold was so sudden and intense that it nipped corn and fruit in the bud.

THE
EIGHTEENTH CENTURY

Frost Fairs and Dust Devils

1716: Worcester Chambers Order – 'Paid several men for many days work in breaking the ice and securing the Worcester Bridge: £1 18s 9d.'

1776: The first week in January saw very wet conditions with some floods, but by the 7th heavy drifting snow had engulfed the two counties with thick, deep drifts. Frost allowed people to walk on the top of the crisp, hard-packed snow. Frost, sleet and snow followed until the 12th, and lanes became blocked and men were unable to work, with drifted snow covering the hedgerows and farm gates. From the 14th the snow continued to pile up, and began to affect the progress of coaches and waggons on the roads. On the 27th snow fell all day and in the evening the frost became intense, while on the 31st the mercury dipped below zero. On 1st February a thaw took place, with flooding and landslides. A hard drought followed, lasting until 30th May.

1795: January and February were plunged into a long and severe frost, with the Wye and the Severn frozen over. A printing press was set up on the ice by Grundy on 25th January, and pig roasts and skating were enjoyed on the frozen Wye near Hereford.

1798: A strong dust devil was seen crossing the Herefordshire countryside just south of Ross-on-Wye. A huge column of dust and debris spiralled upwards to a great height, picking up straw and other items as it passed by. Later in June another was spotted at Droitwich in Worcestershire. It crossed the river Severn at Holt Fleet, picking up a quantity of water and causing it to appear to rain from the clear blue sky as the wind passed through the countryside for another four miles. Enough water fell to give a sharp downpour, complete with rainbow.

1799: A long hot, dry spell suddenly came to an end by the beginning of August, when violent thunderstorms swept into Herefordshire. Huge hailstones three quarters of an inch in diameter stripped the trees of their summer foliage and damaged crops. At one stage it was seen to rain minnows, and the tiny fish covered the ground in a wide swathe.

On 14th May 1886 the Great Flood swept across Worcestershire, one of the worst natural calamities experienced by the county.

THE NINETEENTH CENTURY

20th January 1802: Wind and Fire

Winds reached hurricane strength over Herefordshire and Worcestershire on 20th January, and trees were brought down over a wide area, especially in south-west Herefordshire where several houses were damaged. Six barns were destroyed as the winds grew in strength over the latter part of the day, and overnight the main tempest struck. The great windmill at Kempsey was set on fire by the sails being whirled around too rapidly. Heavy rains added to the misery.

25th January 1805: London Mail Stopped

Early in the morning the east wind blew so strong and cold that it froze the wheels of waggons coming in from the south. Icicles 15 ft long and 9 inches in diameter formed within hours, and ice floated downstream from Hereford and Worcester. By midday the skies had turned a yellowy-grey, becoming almost as black as night. Blizzards then set in from Ludlow in the north to Broadway in the south. Heavy snows prevailed throughout the afternoon, evening and following night, with gale force winds whipping the snow into great drifts 20 ft deep in more rural areas. All travel ceased and the London Mail was unable to get through.

15th July 1808: The Tempest Struck

After a prolonged hot, dry spell the weather broke on the 15th, when the skies over Herefordshire and Worcestershire turned jet black. For about an hour and a half in the early afternoon torrential rains fell, with hundreds of houses flooded to a great depth. Thunder continued in what seemed an unbroken roar throughout the storm and the hailstones that fell were like fragments of a vast plate of ice broken into pieces, they were so broad, flat and ragged.

18th June 1809: Out of the Blue

After a sunny, very warm morning in the Herefordshire countryside, there was a storm of rain, or what appeared to be rain, from a clear blue sky.

As two local farm lads were haymaking, they spotted a huge column of dust, estimated at 200 ft high, meandering its way across the meadow. The light air whipped up within minutes to gale force, snatching up straw and debris. Foliage was stripped from nearby trees, and even a number of haystacks were whirled away. The lads, on horseback, followed the dust devil for five miles. It crossed a nearby lake, taking in a quantity of water. As it headed towards Hay-on-Wye it began to decay, depositing straw, debris and other oddments over a nearby village, together with as much water as might have been expected from a heavy shower. For at least two minutes, rain fell from a clear blue sky.

10th November 1810: Lightning Down the Chimney

A storm hit Herefordshire and Worcestershire with great force, with a number of trees torn up by the roots. The lightning struck

Hylton Road, Worcester during the floods of the late 1890s.

the house of Mr Harris of Edgar Street and came down the chimney of the room in which he was sitting, burning his hand and eyebrows, his stockings and his papers, and tearing down a mirror and a clock from the opposite side of the room.

27th May 1811: The Day it Hailed

A cluster of heavy rain and hail storms swept the area, first ravaging the Worcestershire countryside, then moving over the Malvern range. Hail was recorded the size of golf balls, piling up to a considerable depth. Violent up-draughts within the storm clouds were to blame, with squalls of wind causing damage to trees in full foliage and to crops. The hail also caused a great deal of damage.

4th March 1818: A Most Furious Storm

A storm swept into Herefordshire, with heavy and persistent rain which lasted for six hours. In Worcester the rain fell for eight hours without cease. The Bristol Mail was held up by the rain and flooding for eleven hours.

20th May 1822: Destruction from the Skies

After a fine sunny spell, 20th May began very calm and peaceful, but by afternoon the air was said to hang with heavy moisture. A tall dark cloud was reported on the southern horizon for much of the afternoon, and shortly before teatime a great storm struck, of an electrical power not seen before in the area. Darkness fell, with continuous lightning flashes and a frightening roar of thunder which lasted until the morning. Hailstones lashed the land, piling up to a foot high in places. A violent whirlwind twisted trees out of the ground in north Herefordshire, said to resemble an earth tremor as it sped by.

5th December 1822: Coachman in Trouble

As winds reached hurricane force from the south-west, four barns were destroyed near Ludlow and henhouses were shattered to pieces. The coachman of the Mail was blown off his box and one of the horses dropped dead on arriving, exhausted from battling against the wind.

14th December 1825: A Sign from Above?

A fearful storm moved into the Ross area, causing a great deal of damage and killing ten horses struck by lightning. A whirlwind near Hay-on-Wye killed three people as debris fell from the skies. The storm struck Worcester from the south-west and the lightning displaced a stone about halfway up St Andrew's church spire.

14th January 1826: The Flock Scattered

A storm of hurricane force at about noon was responsible for felling a number of trees, many torn up by the roots, laying walls and fences flat and scattering corn and hay ricks. The wind brought down part of the spire of Cleobury Mortimer church during divine service and the congregation rushed out of the church in terror.

28th-30th December 1836: Whiteout

An extraordinary snowstorm struck just after Christmas, as cold north winds blew and lakes iced over. The Mail was 36 hours late in getting through in many places, with the snow said to have drifted to a depth of 20 ft. Wind whipped up the snow to cover the windward side of houses to roof level, and visibility

GENERAL
HAIL STORM INSURANCE
SOCIETY.

Head Office, Norwich.
London Office, 26, Birchin Lane.

PATRONS.

The Duke of Norfolk
The Earl of Albemarle
The Earl of Abergavenny
The Earl of Orford
The Lord Stafford
The Lord Bayning
Sir Edmund Bacon, Bart.
Sir W. B. Proctor, Bart.
Sir Charles M. Clarke, Bart.
Edmond Wodehouse, Esq. M P.
H. N. Burroughes, Esq. M. P.
Edward Fellowes, Esq. M. P.
R. Sanderson, Esq. M. P.
Edward Bagge, Esq.
T. R. Buckworth, Esq.
J. T. Mott, Esq.

The Earl of Leicester
The Lord Walsingham
The Lord Colborne
The Hon. W. R. Rous
The Hon. Admiral Irby
Sir T. H. E. Durrant, Bart.
Sir W. J. H. B. Folkes, Bart.
Sir E. H. K. Lacon, Bart.
Sir W. Foster, Bart.
W. L. W. Chute, Esq. M. P.
B. Smith, Esq. M. P.
J. B. S. Bradfield, Esq.
H. D'Esterre Hemsworth, Esq.
John Longe, Esq.
Major Loftus
&c. &c. &c.

DIRECTORS.

Samuel Bignold, Esq.
John Wright, Esq.
John Skipper, Esq.
F. J. Blake, Esq.
Roger Kerrison, Esq.

Robert Pratt, Esq.
Thomas Salter, Esq.
James Neave, Esq.
John Cann, Esq.
J. Hilling Barnard, Esq.

BANKERS.
Messrs. Gurneys & Birkbeck.

SECRETARIES.
C. S. Gilman & E. C. Morgan.

The great destruction of property by the Hail Storm on the 9th of August, 1843, which appears to have spread ruin and desolation amongst the Framers and Gardeners in many parts of the Kingdom, more particularly in the Counties of Norfolk, Suffolk, Essex, Cambridge, Bedford, Oxford, and Hertford, has proved the absolute necessity of adopting measures for securing individuals against the pecuniary losses attending these terrific visitations.

Experience has shewn, that Hail Storms, for many years past, have been of more frequent occurrence than formerly. In several cases only partial losses have been sustained, yet there are many instances where farmers and others have had to lament the total destruction of their property ; and although large subscriptions have been raised, yet none sufficiently ample to place these sufferers in their former position, whilst many persons, whose

An insurance prospectus issued shortly after the great hail storms of 9th August 1843. The two counties seem to have escaped the hail storms but on the same date they endured a violent twelve-hour thunderstorm.

was poor in the heavily falling snow, rather as if a fog had descended.

13th June 1839: Hail Six Feet Deep

A thunderstorm crossed Herefordshire and winds gusted to gale force, bringing down trees in full leaf. As it crossed the north of the county a hailstorm of great ferocity raged. The hailstones came down in such numbers that it was widely reported they lay for many hours to a depth of 6 ft. A severe thunderstorm in Worcestershire was followed by rain storms.

9th August 1843: The Sky Glowed

A violent thunderstorm carried on a south-westerly wind lasted for twelve hours. The thunder pealed incessantly and ten houses were struck by lightning in Worcester. At one house in The Shambles, a boy was standing with a knife in his hand when the blade was struck and snapped off. The lightning was so bright and so frequent that it was said that the sky glowed like a pearl.

21st August 1843: A Devil of a Wind

After a hot sunny morning the air temperature reached high levels and the ground was said to be hot enough to fry an egg. The uneven ground temperatures created a gusty wind, and north of Leominster a dust devil was spotted, moving in a northerly direction, emitting a noise like a steam train. As it gained momentum it smashed through a lonely farmhouse and took with it three henhouses. Six sheep, two cows and four goats were killed as debris rained down from the heavens. Dust and paper, hay and straw, were all taken up into its violent circulation, and as it passed over a burning field of stubble it

The product of a more recent hail storm.

sucked up burning straw, starting fires in nearby fields and setting light to hayricks.

4th September 1852: Tornado!

The city of Worcester and the western parts of the county were visited by a tornado on the 4th, said to the worst within living memory and bringing the greatest amount of rainfall in a radius of 20 miles ever previously measured.

About half past six in the evening vivid flashes of lightning lit up the sky, while rolling peals of thunder could be heard rumbling in the distance. Between half past seven and eight o'clock the rain descended in torrents. The water in the Severn rose rapidly, while the neighbourhood brooks were soon filled to overflowing, and the resulting floods were truly fearful, especially in the valley of the river Teme and the vicinity of the Laugherne and Leigh brooks.

The parapets of the bridge at Laugherne brook, erected in 1821, were swept away. In the neighbourhood of Wick the water overflowed gates and hedges and over 150 sheep drowned. At Leigh the bridge was completely dismantled, the water carrying the coping stones and bricks in all directions.

The swirling winds lasted throughout the storm, and a large hay rick was carried over several hedges and deposited in a neighbour's field nearly a quarter of a mile away. The high walls surrounding the garden of Hopton Court were destroyed by the twister and the flood.

In the neighbourhood of Alfrick, at Mill House, the stream carried away a wall 100 ft in length, while a house adjoining the mill was completely ruined, the floors of the lower rooms being swept away together with one end of the house. Powick and the

33

surrounding area suffered greatly too, many houses being flooded and an immense number of sheep drowned, their carcasses discovered afterwards hanging upon the hedges. Damage from both the wind and the floods occurred at Malvern, Whitbourne, Mathon and Cradley, while most places felt some effects from the dreadful storm.

12th November 1852: Coach Washed Away

Torrential rainstorms lashed Herefordshire during November, bringing in their wake flooding and a trail of destruction. The Welsh border and up through the Welsh Marches were the worst affected area, with Ludlow under water, houses flooded, and farmers reflecting on the high prices the waterlogged fields would impose on root crops. The Herefordshire gasworks was flooded and the mail from Worcester to Leominster had to be diverted via Malvern. It was a month to remember, with stories of difficulties on the roads and of tragic drownings.

The London to Aberystwyth mailcoach left the city of Gloucester between one and two o'clock in the morning of the 12th, and took its normal route along the Ledbury Road towards Herefordshire, carrying three passengers and 13 mailbags. Mr Charles Murphy, a coachman of some repute, was at the reins and Mr Couldrey was the guard. Rain soon began to pour down as the journey continued.

At about 5 am, as the coach raced towards the brick-built bridge over the Frome some six miles from Hereford, Mr Couldrey heard Murphy shout out, 'Oh, good God!' The bridge, owned by the Hereford Turnpike Trust, had been washed away during the night and in an instant the front horses were in the deep, swirling water of the river Frome. It was only by a miracle that the cries of distress were heard by John Taylor, keeper of the Longworth

Lodge, who was waiting to collect his master's mailbags from the passing coach.

Taylor alerted his friends, and sent to Mr W.M. Vevers of Bartestree for a horse and cart. Mr Vevers sent his son into Hereford to report the accident and to call upon Mr Evan Williams, surgeon at Lugwardine, to tell him that his services were required. In the heat of the moment, Mr Williams misunderstood the message and went to the Lugg Bridge instead of the Five Bridges, before realising his error. By the time he arrived the leading horses had managed to free themselves, but one, a fine horse called Charity who was well known on the coaching routes for his speed, was drowned.

7th July 1872: The Day of the Whirligig

Typhoons may often bring terror to the tropics, but in 1872 the first ever recorded Herefordshire 'whirligig' flattened much of Felton.

On 7th July the residents of Felton felt something ominous was on the way. A week of intense heat had climaxed in a day of unsettling and threatening gloom, and many of them left their work in the fields and made for home. Peering from the windows, they could see clouds rising and falling in a pillar of fine dust. A sudden whizzing noise was followed by storm winds, loud peals of thunder and vivid, rapid-fire flashes of lightning.

This never to be forgotten storm started in a hollow at Felton Court and then passed up the hillside, thankfully missing the church, the rectory and the noble elms and oaks surrounding them. Roofs were ripped from houses, windows blown out, grain in the fields beaten to the ground, hop poles uprooted and bines smashed to pieces. Cracking trees gave off the most awful

35

sounds parishioners had ever heard. One oak tree with a trunk 50 ft long up to the beginning of the branches and a girth of 6ft 3 inches was simply thrown down at right angles to the track of the storm. Other trees were thrown and twisted in every direction, reflecting the wind's rotary movement.

The *Herefordshire Times* reported: 'The centre of the parish of Felton seems to have experienced all the effects of this tornado, for, as was noticeable in many of the orchards, the trees presented the appearance of a cannon ball having been directly fired through, so completely and regularly were they blown down. That this only extended to one half of the orchards is the most peculiar coincidence. It was said that a colt was blown over a hedge into a pool and that stock ran about in a frightful manner.'

The dimensions of the tornado were comparatively small, but it was the only one recorded at that time in Herefordshire and it wrought mischief on a large scale. It had been preceded by, and was followed by, storms of great violence which gave a third more rainfall than occurred in an average month. The 'whirligig' ruined several orchards, destroying nearly 100 fruit trees in one, smashed barns to smithereens and crushed cottages. Happily not a single soul was killed that day, and even the pigs went on unconcernedly feeding while sty roofs blew away. Ullingswick and Withington are both very close to Felton but suffered not a tossed twig nor a single slipped slate.

December 1879: Glittering Icicles

After one of the coldest recorded spells of weather of the century, surpassed in severity only by the famous Thames Frost Fair of 1814, water in all parts of Herefordshire and Worcestershire froze solid. Icicles formed to a length of 15 ft, measuring 1 ft across at the top. Ice-bound roads brought many reports of broken bones and bruises. The cold began in October and lasted until December, a bitter few months.

10th June 1883: Hit by Heaven's Artillery

The tiny church of Llandinabo stands in a peaceful setting midway between Hereford and Ross-on-Wye, and on a sultry Sunday afternoon in 1883, men, women and children filed in to attend divine worship. Before long they must have been thinking that their hour had come, for the air was rent by what the *Hereford Times* described as 'the artillery of Heaven'.

During the previous two days huge storms had lashed the county, and on this Sunday as the service started the wind was blowing strong and squally and the skies were turning black. Thunder rumbled as the storm arrived from the south. When the service was over many of the congregation remained in the church, loath to go out into the storm which had by now broken. Feeling hot and sticky in their Sunday best, their discomfort soon turned to terror.

A blinding flash of lightning illuminated the interior of the church and simultaneously there was a terrific clap of thunder like the discharge of heavy artillery. The 'electric fluid', as the newspaper described it, caused havoc. A number of people were struck down and at least 20 were 'paralysed by the shock'. Mr Oswell, son of the rector the Reverend Henry Oswell, was among those most affected. Edwin Hyett, the clerk, and his 14 year old son were 'prostrated', the lad being unconscious for hours.

It could have been worse, for one William Matthews who was in the porch had 'induced' some women to return to the church from the ancient yew tree under which they were sheltering. This proved to be a suggestion that probably saved their lives, for just as they scurried the few yards back to the church, the old tree was struck. Mr Matthews and a Mr Morgan suffered severely from the shock, being knocked insensible for a few seconds. But on recovering consciousness they 'rendered assistance to the prostrate women and children in the church and in the kindest manner with as little delay as possible'. Throughout the drama the rain fell in torrents, 'inundating' the roads. There was no weary trudge home for the victims of the elements, however, as Mr Matthews called for his waggonette to be brought to the church to convey the sufferers home.

Eyewitnesses of that amazing storm later said that the lightning or thunderbolt looked like a large ball of dazzling, silvery-blue fire which struck the corner of the church's bell turret.

14th May 1886: The Great Flood

The time of the Great Flood was one of the worst natural disasters Worcestershire has ever known, when virtually the whole of the county was under deep water. Dozens of people were drowned and buildings destroyed. Acres of rich farmland were swept away. Never before had there been such a rapid and disastrous flood, with such loss of life. *Berrows Worcester Journal* of Saturday 22nd May 1886 devoted nearly a whole page of very tiny print to the Great Flood, its headlines screaming of 'Loss Of Life And Terrible Devastation'.

The spring flood came on with startling rapidity after torrential rainstorms, the torrent sweeping over roads, fields and gardens. Animals were carried away by the sheer force of the water, hayricks swept away, crops damaged, hops uprooted and lost, roads washed away and barriers and walls demolished. Tenbury was worst hit by the sudden onrush of flood water, where a lame tailor named William Jones was drowned in his house in Church Street. Hundreds of cheeses, pickles, tinned goods and groceries

Skating on the frozen river Severn at Bewdley in the 1890s.

were to be seen floating down Teme Street after torrents of water smashed the windows of Mr B. Goodall's shop.

At Powick the wife and three children of coachman John Evans were marooned in their cottage near the Yellow Lion Inn, surrounded by deep water. Eventually a young man named Hodges, son of the landlord, was lowered out of one of the windows of the pub with a rope around his waist in a bid to reach the family, but the fast-flowing flood water carried him away and he was only rescued with great difficulty and in a state of exhaustion.

At Alfrick, seven year old Thomas Wood was drowned when he fell from a bridge, and another child named Brooks was drowned in the Stour at Kidderminster. Pigs, rabbits, fowls and ducks were seen floating down the rivers, often to be collected up and thrown into bags. A relief fund was set up in Worcester, with the people of the city and those from the surrounding countryside working together to bring the crisis to an end.

EARLY TWENTIETH CENTURY
1900-1920

Weather Notes 1900-1910

1900: A cold February with snow and ice across the area, and some very strong winds bringing much distress and hardship. A July heatwave set in with an air temperature of 36°C (97°F) at the end of the month.

1901: A good deal of fine and sunny weather through the year. A summer heatwave sent the thermometer up to 34.2°C (94°F) in many places, with 35.5°C (96°F) being reached on 10th August.

1903: An electrical storm hit the area on 2nd November with severe flooding and much damage caused by squally winds, which reached speeds of near hurricane force as a squall line passed through. Many trees were struck in both Herefordshire and Worcestershire, with brooks and streams overflowing from flash floods. Two inches of rain fell in one hour.

1908: After a very warm spell of weather, torrential thunderstorms hit both Herefordshire and Worcestershire with great force. This was on 4th June, the day after the same cloudbursts had wreaked havoc in eastern and north-eastern England. During the day heavy squalls of rain and hail struck most of the county, creating sudden landslides and flood conditions. The

St John's, Worcester, during one of the cold winters of the early 1900s.

wind tore down a large pine tree in the Ludlow area, with many smaller trees being struck by the almost continuous lightning flashes.

Summer 1911: The Big Heat

A record-breaking heatwave made this an outstanding summer for both England and Wales. Persistent high pressure belts predominated, with a scorching sun that shone for long periods of time and gave brilliant blue skies.

Over 1,600 hours of sunshine for the year as a whole made it a record in every sense.

It was fine in May and June, with sunny warm days and light winds. The coronation of George V on 22nd June was celebrated

42

in glorious warm sunshine, ideal for all the parties and displays planned.

The heatwave arrived in July. For days the sun bore down from cloudless blue skies. Many places received just 0.5 inches of rainfall in the whole summer, and rainfall figures were well down in both Herefordshire and Worcestershire, where only 0.25 inches was logged in July.

It was not all good news. People and plants wilted in the torrid heat, and masses of people flocked to the coastal resorts to find cooler sea breezes. The high air temperature combined with the strong sunlight set the death rate soaring and in larger cities such as London the mortality rate rose to 20 per thousand. Cattle perished, food was in short supply and crops failed, and water supplies were at their lowest. In many places the drought and heat brought the worst harvest for 70 years.

The heat became more intense during August with a high of 34°C (93°F) in Herefordshire and 36°C (97°F) in Worcestershire on the 20th. The summer went down in the record books as The Big Heat of 1911, a most remarkable summer that broke many records.

18th June 1911: The Bredon Whirlwind Freak

On 18th June of that glorious summer, a wind of great force swept by Bredon Hill in the Vale of Evesham.

The day began warm and sunny, the Bredon summit just kissed with white mist. As the land heated up with the strong, hazy sunshine of that June day, a thermal breeze began to set in. By afternoon the stubble fires had started, and it was reported that the sky sometimes became obscured by the dense white smoke from the fires.

About four o'clock in the afternoon, the sky turned ebony with a squally wind blowing in the Vale. Thunder was reported towards the south of the hill range. The cloud lowered and brought a sudden wind squall up through the Vale, covering a three mile radius.

The thunderstorm decayed but the squally nature of the wind was extremely odd. It swirled downhill towards the lower lands and as it travelled it gained force. Its twisting effect was most apparent as it entered a woodland region on the east side of Bredon Hill. The trees were stripped of their foliage and a two-mile swathe of destruction saw trees uprooted, hayricks damaged and a farm machine lifted and thrown 25 yards.

A 35 ft column of smoke and fire was consumed by the wind storm, taking it at least 250 yards from the fire's original site. A corn crop was battered to the ground. As the wind hit the valley it bounced across a stream and hit a farmhouse, causing considerable damage to both the house and outbuildings. Suddenly the whirlwind headed off in a north-easterly direction and decayed as rapidly as it had appeared.

1917: A Bitter Cold

A very bitter winter set in after the Christmas period 1916, although many places experienced a white Christmas. During January and February both Herefordshire and Worcestershire suffered severe frosts. During the first ten days of February, the cold was so bitter as to freeze over the Severn and the Wye, with many other waterways packed with ice and snow. The frost lasted from 22nd January to 18th February, with the air temperature falling to a low of −12°C (10°F) on 7th February, 22 degrees of frost.

After the wet month of July, when the men fighting in the third battle of Ypres on the other side of the Channel became bogged down in the Flanders mud, temperatures stayed low in that depressing year.

THE WEATHER IN THE TWENTIES AND THIRTIES

Summer 1921: The Desert Year

Across much of England and Wales, 1921 was called the Desert Year. Only 16.47 inches of rainfall were recorded against the average of 32.50 inches. In June only 0.44 inches fell, and in July only 0.55 inches. A high pressure ridge prevailed for much of the year, with often scorching sunshine and thirsty winds.

The weather had a devastating effect on animal and bird life. June's rainfall, the small amount made up from scattered thunderstorms, rapidly ran off the parched ground without having much effect. By July the grass and woodlands were tinder dry, with fires on farms and embankments especially straining the resources of the firemen.

In Herefordshire streams that normally flowed through the year dried up completely, and in Worcestershire wild fowl died in the countryside for lack of water. Thankfully not so many people died from heat-related diseases as in 1911. One thunderstorm, which produced the only rainfall in the area during July, came from nowhere, with hailstones as big as golf balls striking a two-mile radius north of Ross-on-Wye.

June 1924 — saving his expensive shoes, a barefoot man walks down a flooded street in Worcester.

Three Counties Show marquees at Pitchcroft under water, June 1924.

Summer 1922: Summer's Shot Its Bolt

Summer came in May with an unusual heat so fierce that crops in the fields were scorched and root crops suffered. The air temperature at Worcester and in Broadway topped 32°C (90°F). However, very often it's said that if hot sunny weather arrives in May, then summer has shot its bolt, and in 1922 this was the case. May saw only 1.28 inches of rainfall, and June just 0.69 inches, but July had an impressive 5.21 inches, causing summer flooding and crop failures. Thundery weather through August brought another 3.12 inches of rain to the area. A complete contrast to the summer of the Desert Year!

June 1924: Three Counties Under Water

Heavy June rains caused a freak flood in the city of Worcester and achieved notoriety for submerging the Three Counties Show, held that year on Pitchcroft racecourse. The whole showground

47

was under water to a depth of several feet. *Berrows Journal* of the time reported that 'motor vehicles and drays were chartered from all over the city to rescue prize cattle and sheep and valuable items of equipment and rush them to higher ground. It was a most amazing sight.'

January 1925: Storm and Flood

After a Christmas of gales and floods, during early January 1925 Herefordshire experienced a succession of storms of a ferocity unparalleled for many years. Roads were suddenly submerged, with houses isolated for days, and many residents struggled to remove their furniture to upper rooms to prevent damage. The postal, telegraphic and telephonic systems were interrupted to a varying degree. The evening mail from Hay-on-Wye was unable to get through to the city of Hereford owing to flash floods at Whitney and Letton.

Not for 30 years had such a storm been experienced at Brecon. The river Usk overflowed and farmers in the locality suffered considerable financial loss from the number of animals washed away. People were stranded in their homes and food supplies ran low. One morning tea was provided from Bridge End Hotel, delivered by Mr Charles West and Mr Richardson. An appeal was put out by Nurse Peters to tradespeople of the town for anything they could give, and she made soup which was delivered by Mr Woodman, the butcher, and Mr Price, the Mayor's son.

The torrential rains and floods caused considerable damage to both roads and fields in the Talybon district. While a passenger train was on the line, a landslide covered the track ahead. The driver, William Penry, was unable to see very far ahead owing to the curving track and the blinding storm, and the train ran straight into the mass of earth and mud. The engine and three

48

The Moors, Worcester during the June floods of 1924.

A horse and trap making its way up Croft Road, Worcester in June 1924.

coaches were derailed, and several of the passengers suffered shock.

29th June 1927: The Day the Sun Disappeared

Weather expert Mr Freddie Parsons of Ross-on-Wye promised all a chance to witness the sensational sight of the total eclipse of the sun, the first of its kind for more than 200 years and a phenomenon not to be seen again in this country for another seven decades.

The Lugg Meadows were packed with residents from Hereford and the surrounding area – the first to arrive was a city librarian with photographic equipment. Bromyard Downs filled with cars and observers. From the nearby Hereford Training College, youngsters took their positions on the college balconies and looking through the windows.

Hereford was just outside the area where the eclipse would be total, but the disc of the sun promised to be almost blocked out. As more of the sun disappeared, and at about 6.20 am the morning light turned to twilight, the birds ceased to sing. A few seconds after 7.15 am the light once more became natural, and the wonderful corona burst forth and silver and gold rays spread across the skies. The world appeared to be on fire, and as the corona died away the sun's return was greeted by the onlookers.

Most of the county turned out to witness this marvellous event. A splendid view was had from many points in Ross, where sightseers scrambled onto rooftops. Some took their position on the tower of St Mary's church and others chose Penyard Wood and Linton Hill. At Llandrindod Wells 1,000 people crowded onto the golf course, and numerous vantage points around Hay-on-Wye were full, including Mouse Castle, Cusop Hill, Hay Common and the Begwyns at Clyro.

Freddie Parsons, who had done much to create this enthusiasm, continued to be a marvel of meteorology, working at the Ross Observatory well into his eighties. Freddie's devotion to duty saw him awarded the MBE, but he is sadly no longer with us.

The rest of that year turned out wet and dismal in many parts and this was blamed on the eclipse of the sun. However, it did end with a real old-fashioned white Christmas. Herefordians spent the greater part of the Christmas period indoors, with newspapers confirming 'Fireside The Best Place In Bitter Weather'.

The Herefordshire countryside, as the rest of the country, received its snowy mantle at the eleventh hour. The arctic winds brought snow on Christmas Day, with buildings and streets soon clothed in white. By the evening snow lay several inches deep, and with the onset of gale force winds drifts to several feet piled up. Blizzards kept many people away from church, with very small congregations reported, and Boxing Day events such as the meet of the South Herefordshire Hounds and football matches were called off.

8th June 1930: It's Raining Periwinkles!

Cumulus cloud early that morning enhanced the otherwise blue sky, with a gentle airflow which seemed to be extremely variable in direction. By late morning a small squall had been spotted out to the south-west. The sky became jet black at noon, and a sudden shower fell first on the Herefordshire countryside, then over Worcestershire. With great force, periwinkles fell from the skies, bouncing off roads and pavements with a loud cracking sound. This was experienced in several places, from Kington in Herefordshire to Stratford-upon-Avon.

This kind of phenomenon occurs when strong up-draughts from cumulonimbus clouds suck various objects up and transport them elsewhere. Going back in time, a similar case is said to have taken place in the St John's area of Worcester. A man named Maund, a meteorologist, went out into the street, now appropriately named Maund Street, and collected enough winkles to fill at least two sacks, which he then took to the local market and sold.

25th August 1935: Waterspout Freak

After a fine spell of weather, a day of unusual events took place over parts of the local area. A funnel cloud was spotted over a large lake near Droitwich which travelled across the meadows nearby before tipping into and across the lake. It snatched up into its circulation some hayricks which then spiralled upwards with great speed. As the hay hit the top of the vortex it was thrown outwards, and came gently down to be sprinkled over the surface of the lake.

As the whirlwind hit the lake it created a wall of water which rose to a great height before being thrown from the top. Small fishing boats and rowing boats on the lake were tossed about with frightening force. The whirlwind lost height dramatically as it travelled towards the far side of the lake, but at the same time water was still being tossed outwards at great speed and the wind was reported to be making a very loud hissing sound.

Later that day another two waterspouts were spotted in other parts of the county, one also being seen on the river Avon close by Evesham. It was certainly something of a freakish period in weather terms to have so many spouts logged in the same day.

THE WEATHER
IN THE FORTIES

28th January 1940: Snapped Off Like Carrots

After a month of bitter cold, snow, wind and freezing rain, the end of January saw surfaces become ice rinks as the heavy snows of weeks past turned to rain in the milder Atlantic air flowing in from the south-west.

As it pushed into the colder, denser arctic air from the Continent, the rain turned readily to freezing rain. It encased telephone wires and the branches of trees, snapping them off like crisp carrots with the sheer weight of the ice. As the rain came into contact with the very cold ground, glaze ice formed on the pavements and the roads and many cases were reported of people with cracked or broken bones from falls. Traffic accidents were also common in the treacherous conditions.

During this bitterly cold month ice formed on all our rivers and Mrs Powell of Eardisley reported that 'after the rain everything froze. It was quite frightening to be outside where tree branches were cracking and falling with the weight of ice and there was a gloomy fog all around. It was very cold.'

Many trees, like this oak in Rectory Meadow, Dorstone, suffered severe damage from ice rain and glaze ice in January 1940.

January 1941: Even the Coal Froze

Another bitterly cold month with wind, snow and frost. Smog was reported on many days, especially in the towns. A yellow-coloured fog affected parts of west Herefordshire, said to be caused by air pollution under anticyclonic conditions. Ice predominated throughout the month, causing much hardship. Coal was reported to be freezing solid out in the open stock yards.

September 1946: Hopfield Havoc

Torrential downpours and high winds whipped through the hopfields in early autumn. Mr E.L. Jay's farm at Leigh Sinton was extensively damaged, leaving the hopfields looking as if they had been hit by a bomb. Winds gusted to hurricane force as the

There was always shanks' pony — a family outing during the winter of 1947.

rains set in, and once the strings of the hops were broken, huge areas of foliage collapsed. Mr H.E. Powell of Upper Wick said that most of his hops were down and elsewhere it was the same story, with growers complaining that their crops had been damaged and bruised, especially in the Worcester area.

1947: That Notorious Winter

The winter of 1947 is still considered by many to be the worst in living memory, coming as it did after five long years of war and privation. January began normally enough, with some very mild and spring-like days, and the terrible weather which followed came as a dreadful shock.

On Monday the 6th snow fell across much of the area but a thaw soon set in. Some mild days followed but on the 25th a Siberian anticyclone brought bitter winds, ice, snow and gales in blizzard conditions. For the next two months they prevailed, before melting snow and heavy rain brought flooding to add to the misery. Much of Herefordshire and Worcestershire was cut off by drifts 12 to 15 ft deep, transport was affected and factories and offices went without power for long periods of time to conserve fuel supplies. Mrs Jean Turner of Cranham Drive, Worcester, remembers that the cold spell came almost overnight, without warning. One of the first problems that arose was that the coal in stock in the sidings at Shrub Hill station could not be moved due to the treacherous condition of the roads. Homes were unheated and icicles hung down outside the windows, some 3 inches in diameter, making it seem as if you were in gaol looking out through the bars.

By 30th January the area was like an arctic wasteland. Schools soon began closing and the problems of transporting fuel and food supplies became ever greater. In Herefordshire and Worcestershire the air temperature fell to −10°C (14°F) on that

A train stuck in the snow between Greens siding and Clifford, 11th March, 1947.

day, with 18 degrees of frost. Ice began to form on rivers and streams, and the surface of the snow froze so hard that people were able to walk over the tops of the hedgerows and snowed-in cars.

Early February brought more severe blizzards, persistent frosts – and chaos! Frozen points added to the problems on the railways and coal stocks were low. Snow ploughs often found themselves in trouble on snowbound roads. A lorry was completely buried as high winds whipped up huge drifts, and many people were treated for frostbite. By mid February blizzards had brought the area to a standstill, with schools and much of industry shut down.

On 25th February the thermometer plummeted to −15°C (5°F), 27 degrees of frost. Drifts of up to 25 ft deep could be found across Herefordshire and winds reached storm force, seriously affecting visibility. Towards the end of February air temperature

Italian POWs clearing snow at Ullingswick during the record-breaking winter of 1947.

levels were still at −14°C (7°F), with icicles everywhere. A thaw was predicted − but the worst was not over yet.

4th March 1947: Whiteout!

The predicted thaw failed to materialise, instead a blizzard struck the Kidderminster area with strong winds blowing the snow into huge drifts varying from 2 to 12 ft deep, cutting off roads and bringing traffic to a standstill. By the Wednesday morning there was widespread chaos once again and many bus services had to be suspended. Train services were disrupted, and newspapers and mail arrived several hours late. On 7th March the temperature again fell to −15°C (5°F). It was yet another winter whiteout.

At Clows Top a telephone kiosk was buried and the road beyond Far Forest was completely blocked, cutting off Cleobury

Convoys of vehicles were formed up to negotiate the flooded roads and to deliver vital foodstuffs and essential workers.

A dramatic rescue in Severn Street, Worcester during the March floods of 1947.

Mortimer for the second time within a month. Cleobury Mortimer's licensing sessions, fixed for Wednesday, had to be adjourned and the cattle market which was to have been held the same day was postponed for a week because of the impossibility of traffic getting through to the village. At Chelmarsh the milk-collecting service had to be abandoned for the same reason. At Sally Bush the drifts were so deep that the roadside hedges were completely obliterated, and only telegraph poles indicated the course of the road.

The earliest bus routes to be affected were those to Ludlow, Tenbury, Clows Top, Stourport to Worcester, Bayton and Bliss Gate. The London daily papers did not reach Kidderminster until late afternoon on the Wednesday, after an eight hour journey

Emergency food supplies being delivered by boat to those cut off from essential services. The local fire service and the WVS are lending a hand here during the floods of March and April, 1947.

from Birmingham to Kidderminster, with Mucklow Hill and Hagley Bank impassable.

At Shatterford on Thursday a 200 yard long drift varying between 4 and 6 ft deep, completely cut off the main Kidderminster to Bridgnorth road. A bus which attempted to get through became stranded and a snow plough was rushed to the spot, with German prisoners of war to help with the digging, to try and open up the road, but it was still blocked that night. German prisoners were also called upon to help clear the streets of Droitwich and in the words of one resident, 'they got a move on'.

Clifton-on-Teme was cut off on Wednesday, when drifted snow was reported to be waist high in the roads, and in some places up to shoulder height. People could not see out of their windows. Residents of Cradley and neighbouring villages woke up on Thursday to find their homes cut off. Drifts up to the level of bedroom windows were a common sight at hillside cottages.

A well known Worcester doctor arrived on skis at Worcester Royal Infirmary, where he later performed an operation. At West Malvern there were snowdrifts 9 to 10 ft deep.

March and April 1947: Water, Water Everywhere

At last came the thaw, but with it came torrential rainfall, a sure recipe for disaster. Rivers and streams rose rapidly and overspilled their banks, while thawing snow created floods in every part of Herefordshire and Worcestershire.

In 1947 the city of Worcester, ravaged by flooding from the river Severn over the centuries, suffered the record floods of our time. A rapid thaw and exceptional rainfall combined with melting snow from the Welsh mountains to submerge the city. The most dramatic effect was to virtually cut off St John's, a third of the city. Worcester Westside was sandwiched between the swollen rivers Severn and Teme and was almost an island.

The New Road flooded to a depth of 7 or 8 ft, and a Dunkirk-style operation had to be used for several days to ferry people between St John's and the city by coach, open-backed lorry and horse-drawn cart. A shuttle train service, free of charge between Foregate Street station and Henwick Halt, gave another vital line of communication. The platforms at both stations were constantly full. The WVS and other voluntary organisations also ferried food and supplies by boat to people marooned in their homes.

THE WEATHER
IN THE FIFTIES

February 1950: Wind and Hail

Between 1st and 15th February strong, stormy winds and torrential rainstorms caused devastation. A whirlwind struck the area between the Black Mountains and Hay-on-Wye, bringing down trees and damaging farm buildings. Hail an inch in circumference fell from the skies, depositing a layer 2 inches deep in places. As the storm moved across the countryside, Mrs Bradley of Hereford was caught by the freak wind and hailstorm. 'It was a frightening experience,' she said. 'The hail blew hard in my face, causing bruising and cuts.'

Heavy downpours locally and upstream in Wales caused the rivers Wye and Severn to rise rapidly. Flooding was commonplace and considered to be the worst since 1947. Large tracts of meadowland were awash with flooded homes, with many houses in Hylton Road and Tybridge Street, Worcester flooded. Water poured across the county cricket ground and the bus station and into the cattle market. Conditions worsened, and a postman and baker made deliveries from a punt. At Upton-on-Severn a chicken pen came down the river with a cat on top. A chair and a large tree were seen to float under Worcester Bridge.

August 1950: Lightning Havoc

In the grounds of the Chateau Impney Hotel at Droitwich, a charred stump about 20 ft high was all that was left of a 60 ft Wellingtonia after a violent thunderstorm hit the area at teatime in late August. After the lightning strike, pieces of the tree were scattered over 100 yards, and the main trunk crashed down across the hotel drive, completely blocking it.

The wind had risen to great speeds in sudden squalls that August afternoon. There were hundreds of lightning strikes reported, homes damaged and trees shattered. Nearly an inch of rain fell within half an hour, causing flash flooding as many streams burst over onto roads.

24th March 1951: All Fair But the Weather

Torrential rain flooded the racecourse at Worcester on 24th March, surrounding the Easter Fair with water several feet deep. Hundreds of pounds worth of business was lost, and showpeople could only stand and watch as the water swirled in around the flying horses and amusements. The steady downpour through Good Friday kept people away from the Easter attractions. The county cricket ground was under water, and the Midland Red Bus Company said that the holiday weekend was a complete washout.

May 1952: Rain Stopped Play

Rainstorms lashed the area during 4th and 5th May, with up to 2 inches of rainfall recorded. Waterlogged ground became a serious problem, and the Severn was reported to be slowly rising. Vale of Evesham growers stated that the continuing wet weather

Worcestershire CCC vice-captain Reg Perks tries his hand at a spot of angling during what should have been the first day's play against the Indian tourists at the New Road ground on 5th May, 1952.

was likely to cause a shortage of spring vegetables as onions and radishes were stunted in their growth, and sprouts were seen to be standing in feet of water. Germination and growth of many crops was adversely affected. The incessant rains also caused flooding at the county cricket club at Hylton Road, Worcester, making play impossible.

2nd January 1954: A Peasouper

Visibility was reduced to zero during the night of 1st January and the following morning, bringing traffic to a grinding halt. Large areas were affected by a yellowy-white pall of fog, which brought a marked increase in the number of chest infections reported. Ice also formed that night, especially on the Malvern to Worcester road.

25th January 1954: Snow Joke

A heavy rainstorm struck Herefordshire on the night of 25th January, so people were surprised to wake up the next morning to find a mantle of snow to a depth of 6 inches!

The snowstorms started in the early hours of the 26th and snow fell so heavily that despite the wet ground surface, it rapidly settled. Snow blanketed the county, and several hamlets, especially in the Black Mountains, were cut off by 4 ft drifts. Snow ploughs and gangs of workmen were soon out working to clear the roads, and on the Hereford to Wye road telephone wires collapsed under the weight of the snow. Buses took five hours to complete a normally simple, 42 mile route. The Hereford to Ross route via Hoarwithy was suspended due to the bad conditions. Yet despite the bitterness of the weather, the sudden snowy conditions were enjoyed by many.

November 1954: Rushing Torrents

On 25th November acres of farmland in Herefordshire and Worcestershire were under water, with livestock having to be moved to higher terrain. Torrential rain, especially in the upper reaches of the county, brought a surge of water downriver.

The racecourse at Pitchcroft, Worcester was under several feet of water, and the river Severn rose to 11 ft 3 inches above normal and was still rising. A herd of cattle was marooned for several hours near the river. The National Hunt meeting fixed for that Saturday could not take place, making it the fourth Worcester race meeting to be abandoned that month. Meanwhile in Herefordshire, the river Wye was reported to be 13 ft above its summer level. Up to 2 inches of rain fell on the area, with up to 3 inches in the hills.

On the 27th the spell of heavy rain was joined by strong, gale force winds. Anemometers logged windspeeds of up to 80 mph. Trees were brought down in their hundreds across western England and Herefordshire and Worcestershire had their fair share of damage. The floods were still high, the rivers still rising, and this was considered the worst flooding to hit the area since February 1950.

26th November 1954: A Ball of Fire

A ball of fire raced across the skies at a rapid speed during a violent thunderstorm on the night of 26th November. A group of girls returning home from Eastnor, near Ledbury were frightened by it.

Miss Nesta Bumfrey recalled: 'We were walking home down Clenchers Mill Lane, Eastnor, near Ledbury soon after six o'clock with our heads down because of the driving rain and flood water on the road, when suddenly we felt a current of heat come down upon us and through the darkness the sky was brilliantly lighted. I looked up and saw what looked like a ball of fire sweeping across the sky at great speed. It seemed to be falling ahead of us in the direction of Bromsberrow. Almost immediately the ground shook under our feet and we were all very frightened.'

Miss Humphries, postmistress of Eastnor post office, said: 'I was indoors at the time. There was a terrific noise like an aeroplane falling. A blue light flashed through the window and the house seemed to shake.' A Bromsberrow resident, however, said, 'We heard a loud bang, but saw nothing else.'

Winter 1954: Roses in Winter

During the extremely mild winter, it was reported that roses bloomed out of season in Cripplegate Park, Worcester, with the rose-bed outside the main gate creating most interest among passers-by and those travelling by bus. Many people stopped to admire the flowers, which were in full bloom in December and January. A brief spell of cold weather discouraged the roses a little, but then more buds appeared once the cold snap was over.

4th January 1955: Blizzards Follow Floods

After end of the year floods, blizzards struck the area on 4th January. Winds whipped the snow into 12 ft drifts in places in Herefordshire, cutting off lanes and making travel by motor and on foot extremely difficult.

The snow began to fall just before ten o'clock, and was already quite a depth by midday. It was reported that the canteen of Croft Mill was wrecked when the gale that accompanied the snow blew down a 27 ft wall. Heavy snow also fell for long periods in Malvern, causing problems there, and many telephone lines were brought down in Evesham. Sporting events were disrupted, including the following night's match at Edgar Street where the University of Wales was due to meet English Universities.

2nd August 1959: The Day it Rained Sticklebacks

A gathering wind storm to the west of Broadway brought an interesting meteorological event to Evesham. After the heat of that glorious summer, a whirlwind or dust devil occurred just to the south of the town.

About four o'clock in the afternoon, a sudden wind arose with such force that it caused great damage to fruit trees in the local orchards of the Vale. As the wind passed by, fish were seen to cover the ground, still very much alive and wriggling.

On inspection they turned out to be sticklebacks. They had been sucked up by the twisting wind storm and carried off, only to be thrown down six miles away from their original source. They were swept up and it was reported that twelve buckets were filled with these tiny fish.

The Stank at Hampton Bishop on the river Wye. Here workmen from the Wye River Board are strengthening the bank during the floods of December 1964.

THE WEATHER
IN THE SIXTIES

December 1960: So Near to Disaster

During December exceptionally high water in the rivers Wye and Lugg nearly brought disaster to the village of Hampton Bishop. The 12 ft embankment known as the Stank, built centuries before to protect the village from the flooding by which it was periodically threatened, gave way in some places and water poured through the village streets. Troops were brought in to help evacuate people from their homes. However, bad as it was it could have been so much worse – the Stank had saved the village from the floods of 1947 and it still held in 1960 to prevent a real disaster.

Major G.N. Croker, a consultant engineer, in a letter to the Wye Catchment Board praised the men who had originally built the Stank. 'As this portion of the Stank was constructed some centuries ago, it is an outstanding example of sound, thorough workmanship and splendid design. I pay my most sincere tribute to those who constructed it, and who by their magnificent work, saved Hampton Bishop from a great catastrophe.'

His letter continued by referring back to the events of 1947 when the Stank held firm. 'Yet again, in the last few days the Stank has proven its worth. For it was the Stank that saved Hampton

The Belmont Road roundabout, Hereford. A gallant 'copper' carries an ill-shod shopper across the road.

Bishop when it was within a hairsbreadth of disaster. If the Stank had not held, the whole village would have been swamped by a devastating wall of water. It is to those ancient dyke builders that the villagers of Hampton Bishop owe their escape. Though the floods have done much damage it could so easily have been a disaster.'

72

A motor-cyclist and his helmet-less passenger tackle the floods at Belmont Road Garage, Hereford during the floods of 1965.

Bernard Colley (left) leads his boys out for some impromptu practice on the streets of Hereford, December 1965.

The rush hour in Hereford on the morning after the night before —
10th December, 1965.

After the flood in 1960 the Stank was repaired and raised by
another 15 inches above the flood level.

Winter 1962-63: The Coldest Since 1740

In many parts of the country the winter of 1962-63 was the
coldest since 1740, even colder than the 1946-47 freeze. Rivers
froze and ice even appeared in the salty waters around the coast.

During December the arctic grip took hold, with dense fog
keeping the temperature well below freezing and visibility down
to zero feet in parts, especially in the larger cities. Towards
Christmas week many places recorded air temperatures down to
−8°C (18°F). Numerous places saw snow before Christmas.

Easterly winds from the Russian Steppes swept across the UK bringing frequent snow storms of great force. The winds whipped up the snow into great drifts in Herefordshire and Worcestershire, blocking roads and creating havoc throughout that winter. On occasions a thaw with rain was forecast, only for heavy snowfalls and severe frosts to take place.

On a few days the milder Atlantic air just made it in across the cold ground, giving a slight thaw but with freezing rain. Then back came the blizzards with greater intensity. The air temperature at noon was often well below zero. The cold froze milk bottles solid, pushing off their foil tops with the cream at the top expanding outwards. Snow cleared by householders became piled 12 ft high at the side of roads, and the grey and yellow skies gave very bad visibility as the snowstorms swept in.

Towards the end of December the temperature dipped to −14°C (7°F) causing frozen pipes and even more chaos on the roads. An area of low pressure down to the south-west approaches to Britain unleashed a severe blizzard, and with storm-force winds huge drifts piled up. More than 90,000 miles of road were snowbound throughout the country.

January was bitterly cold, and as we headed into the new year an easterly wind set in. Many parts of the country braved heavy snowfalls, bitter winds, blocked roads and general hardship. Food and other items were in short supply, and coal froze solid in the sidings with the thermometer down to −17°C (1°F) on many days.

The temperature often only reached −4°C (25°F) with almost every day bringing some heavy snow. This often began to fall in the later afternoon and continued through the night and into the next morning, with a brief respite between late morning and the next fall. Severe arctic conditions continued through February with frequent blizzards, very low air temperatures and bitter winds and frosts.

75

Madge Hooper standing on the frozen river Wye at Fownhope in February, 1963.

A 'submerged' signpost at Hegdon Hill, Pencombe, February 1963. The snow remained in roadside ditches until May that year.

The thaw arrived after a few more days of winter in early March. There were no prolonged heavy rains as in 1947, so the thaw came in with gentle, mild spring sunshine. Temperatures gradually climbed to 7°C (45°F) on the 6th and 7th, and peaked at just over 60°F later in the month.

February 1969: Blizzard Chaos

After a mild end to January, with air temperatures peaking at a record January reading for both Herefordshire and Worcestershire of 15°C (59°F), a much colder frosty spell of weather set in from 1st February, with severe night frosts.

The temperature dropped to −8°C (18°F) on the 7th. There was some sunshine but the temperature stayed well below freezing all day, with blizzards blocking off roads, disrupting traffic and causing numerous problems with power supplies. In Worcestershire drifts were commonplace, while over in Herefordshire huge drifts piled up to 10 ft high covering cars and hedgerows. The northerly winds reached speeds of up to 55 mph in exposed parts.

On 18th February the easterly wind from the Russian Steppes pushed very cold Arctic continental air in across the area, bringing with it gales of up to 65 mph and air temperatures overnight of −2°C (28°F). Light snow fell in the wind but the forecast was for no real snowfall overnight. Then during the early hours of the 19th the snow began to fall heavily with the bitter winds prevailing. Blizzards set in, giving a level snow cover of 6 inches in the Worcestershire area and drifts of over 6 ft. There was chaos on the roads, with many rural routes declared impassable by the police and AA. Over the Malvern Hills drifts of up to 10 ft were reported in places, and many roads were blocked and unsafe.

14th June 1969: The Day It Rained Red Worms

After an extremely thundery spell of weather at the end of May, which gave nine consecutive days of thundery activity and over 5 inches of rain, June saw fine hot spells with air temperatures reaching 80°F or 90°F on some days.

However, after another very hot day on 14th June, with a maximum of 32°C (90°F) the sky developed the classical signs of a thundery breakdown by late morning. By 3 pm the first rumbles of thunder were heard to the south-east, reminding everyone that a heavy storm was brewing. At that time the wind direction was east to north-east and very light.

At 4.30 pm thunder was still rumbling around to the south of the county, though the storm had still not broken in this area. A report at about 6 pm confirmed our conclusion that the storms were holding across the Cotswolds and the east to south-east wind was blowing from the north-east above us in the upper atmosphere. Our numerous reporting weather stations to the south began measuring their first rain from the edge of the storms at 7 pm. The large, towering thunderhead clouds moved in, bringing some violent bursts of rain and hailstones.

During the evening we received reports that red worms had fallen from the skies in villages just north of the Cotswolds. Our crew travelled down to the area to find small red worms in great numbers covering the roads and footpaths. The thunderstorm cloud responsible had moved away to the north-west, but we followed the storm cell just in time before it decayed. Falling within the rain were red worms. They had obviously been lifted from some point by the strong up-draughts of the storm, transported to the area and deposited within the down-currents. This went into the logbook as The Day It Rained Red Worms.

Bricks were thrown 25 yards as the January 1976 hurricane demolished Hallow school hall. This was the worst hurricane on record in the area.

80

THE WEATHER
IN THE SEVENTIES

7th May 1970: Hailstorm Havoc

From 3rd May we enjoyed hot weather, with air temperatures in my thermometer screen in south Worcester peaking at 30.5°C (87°F). Then on 7th May, with a barometer reading of 29.7 inches at 8 am, a high humidity figure of 92% and a light south/south-easterly airflow from France, we logged all the signs of a thundery breakdown later that day.

After a sunny morning with hardly a cloud to be seen, thundery looking cloud formed which gave a most chaotic but tropical look to the skyscape, a forewarning of the storms not far off. By 3 pm the cloud had turned dark with the large anvil-type vertical storm cloud we 'in the business' call cumulonimbus showing up nicely to the south. The first rumbles of thunder sounded over the countryside. Vivid lightning displays flashed from the storm clouds gathering to the east. Dogs in the vicinity became disturbed as the thunder moved closer.

Reports of severe flooding with squalls and hailstorms were soon being logged at the weather station. At that time the thermometer was still high, producing enough heat to fuel the storm cells.

Before the warm spring and scorching summer of 1976, we had a cold February – this remarkable cascading icicle was reported on 3rd February, 1976.

82

A tree felled by freak winds wrecked this car in a park at Ross-on-Wye, 9th January 1975.

The storm broke over the area at about 4.30 pm, when vivid lightning bolts caused damage to property and struck numerous trees. At least three thunderbolts were spotted across various parts of the country, varying from a red and orange glow to violet and yellow streaks. One farmhouse near Tewkesbury was hit and sustained considerable damage.

Torrents of rain fell, giving between 1 and 2 inches and producing flash floods, with flood water within the drainage systems pushing off the heavy manhole covers and creating a fountain of water 6 ft high in places. Squalls of up to 50 mph accompanied the storms, and at about 5 pm large hailstones fell from the skies over several parts of the county. At the Worcester station they measured an inch in diameter, smashing glasshouses and frames and stripping foliage from the trees nearby. The hail lay to a depth of 2 inches and resembled a heavy snowfall, taking about two hours to completely melt away.

Repair work under way in the county after the New Year storm of 1976.

Summer 1976: What A Scorcher!

No summer in past years has matched up to 1976. It was a scorcher and a classic, with endless Mediterranean blue skies, very little rainfall and blistering heat which made the countryside resemble a desert as lawns and grassland shrivelled and forest and woodland areas became tinder dry and a high fire risk.

With east to north-east winds during May, the rainfall was below average. The ground began to dry out at a tremendous rate as evaporation rates soared following the drought conditions of 1975 and a winter that had been also very dry. By June Herefordshire and Worcestershire had joined the rest of England and Wales in severe drought conditions. The daytime air temperature peaked at 32.9°C (91°F) on the 28th. The few storms which broke through the month did little to help the drought conditions. With the hot sun and dry air (humidity levels were by day often down to 25%) any water which reached the ground rapidly evaporated away.

Into July the heat intensified, with the thermometer peaking in Hereford and Worcester city centres at 34.1°C (93°F) on the 3rd. Streams dried out, rivers were running low and grazing land for livestock became barren desert. Eight consecutive days with air temperatures at or above 30°C caused concern as the hosepipe ban continued, and problems arose in getting water supplies up into the higher areas.

On some days thunder and lightning was recorded, but due to the very dry surface air by the time the rain from the gathering storm clouds could reach the ground it had evaporated, to give what we then called a dry thunderstorm. As the hot sun beat down, the tinder-dry countryside was often ablaze, with fires raging out of control. On many days a white pall of smoke could be seen for miles around coming up from the Malvern Hills,

Desperate measures — lending a hand at a blaze on the Malvern Hills, during the long hot summer of 1976.

where our local firemen were stretched to their limits of endurance.

During August there was little rain and sweltering blue skies prevailed. The reservoirs were extremely low and with

Nunnery Wood, Worcester, summer 1976. This picture captures a lightning discharge and the vivid return stroke.

The drought-hit reservoir at British Camp, Malvern, during the 1976 scorcher.

weathermen seeing no end in sight to the blistering heat there was great concern about water supplies right across England and Wales. Many of the Welsh reservoirs which supply Herefordshire and Worcestershire were becoming dangerously low, with some drying up completely, their clay bottoms cracking open.

The government became very concerned at the worsening water crisis and in that scorching summer Dennis Howell MP became 'Minister for Drought'. Millions of people were faced with water rationing and standpipes were introduced to conserve supplies. Worcester City Council fought water leaks with a vengeance and gave top priority to overflow pipes and cracked lavatories. The race committee succumbed to pressure and turned off their irrigation system on 27th August. A ban on cleaning cars and topping up swimming pools and fishponds was introduced. After

A giant cedar tree falls victim to a lightning strike during the night of 24th September, 1976.

Feast or famine – flooded meadows by the Wye, February 1979.

15 months of the driest weather on record, farm produce was lost, industry was hit, wildlife killed off and health threatened – many people suffered from heat stroke and heart attacks brought on by the heat. The crisis was estimated to have cost the country some £500 million.

Some rain fell across Herefordshire and Worcestershire at the end of August with a thundery breakdown to the summer heatwave giving flash floods and at least 2 inches of rain over that Bank Holiday weekend. At last the end of the drought was in sight.

September 1976: The Deluge Begins

The heavens opened on 24th September, with hail, lightning and thunder. Many parts of Herefordshire and Worcestershire suffered flash flooding as up to 6 inches of rain fell over the next couple of days, blocking roads and causing landslides.

Homes were flooded over a wide area, with firemen answering many calls for help. There was over 5 ft of water in the shops in Commercial Road, Hereford. On Whitecross Road a family who had turned their cellar into a garage found their Mini covered by water which had swept down the ramp. Belmont roundabout and Ledbury Road were under water. Muddy waters running off a nearby building site swamped houses in Treago Close, Newton Farm. Several cars got stuck in flood water at Eardisley. Ross-on-Wye was also badly hit, and the Hereford to Ross road was blocked at Much Birch after a landslide.

It was reported that with a fifth of that year's rainfall falling over that weekend, the dried up rivers were filling up again. The drought was officially declared over on 8th October after a succession of monsoon-like downpours which gave the wettest autumn on record.

THE WEATHER
IN THE EIGHTIES

Winter 1981/2: An Arctic Scene

From 8th to 19th December bitter Arctic winds blew across Herefordshire and Worcestershire, bringing with them heavy blizzards and deep snows. The air temperature fell to its lowest on the 12th with an overnight low and record of −17.6°C (1°F). Freezing fog brought traffic almost to a standstill on the 10th with visibility down to 15 yards in places. Heavy drifting snow on that night lasted well into the morning of the 11th, blocking roads and closing down schools. Severe blizzards caused huge drifts 12 ft high in places, especially over the open, higher terrain of Herefordshire.

There was a milder spell over Christmas but during early January the bitter weather returned with a vengeance. Heavy snow fell on the night of the 7th with a strong, bitter east wind creating huge drifts 25 ft high in places, cutting off villages, bringing traffic to a standstill and once again closing schools. On the 9th the severe cold and blizzards prevailed, followed over the next three days by fine but extremely frosty weather. The night temperature fell to its lowest on the 13th with a reading of −17°C (1°F).

The frozen river Teme at Powick in the cold spell of 1981.

Thawing snow and heavy rain during late December 1981 brought a landslide of mud down across this country road in Worcestershire.

Nine stranded horses had to be rescued at Lower Ham, Kempsey in November 1984.

Air temperatures by day stayed well below freezing level during this period, with a maximum thermometer reading of only −8.2°C (17°F) on the 13th and a maximum temperature of −7°C (19°F) on the 14th. In the clear crisp daytime frost, the air temperature was so low on the days when the sun shone that 'diamond dust' could be seen scintillating in the air. On the 16th the snow began to melt as milder unsettled Atlantic air flowed in across the country.

December 1982: An Ill Wind

Early in December 1982 a wind of hurricane force whipped across north Herefordshire. Winds reached speeds of 90 mph over open ground, wrecking a family home and leaving a mile-long trail of destruction. Farmers Aubrey and Gillian Roberts

A huge drift towers over a country lane after seven hours of snowfall on 8th February 1985.

and their three children were forced to move out of their partially destroyed Shobdon home at Lower Ledicott Farm following the freak wind, which struck at teatime.

Mrs Roberts and her daughters Julia and Anna stood in the kitchen of their home and prayed as the howling wind tore the farmhouse apart, reported the *Herefordshire Times*. The tornado-like wind lasted three to four minutes. The electricity failed and there was flashing outside as the cables were ripped down, and they could hear the sound of smashing glass.

Thousands of pounds worth of damage was caused to their home. A large plate glass window was smashed and cracks appeared in walls. Upstairs a bedroom door was blown across a landing. By the light of day they found that roof tiles weighing over 10 lbs had been carried over two fields by the wind, and cavity wall-filling littered the hedges. Their pet rabbit had disappeared from its cage, a garden pergola had been flattened and a free-standing swimming pool battered.

February 1985: Snowed Under

On 8th February a seven-hour snowfall brought huge drifts to the county, blocking country lanes. Later another 13 hours of snowfall created drifts from 4 ft to 12 ft deep in country areas as the strong winds whipped the snow into giant piles for days after the main blizzards had passed on the 10th.

29th July 1985: The Upton Snodsbury Funnel Cloud

Mr John Spicer of Malvern Wells writes that while travelling west on the A422 on 29th July, he saw a tornado funnel cloud. It was first visible when passing near Upton Snodsbury at 11 am,

The winter of 1988/9 – snow on a border road.

97

though it was several miles away to the west or south-west initially.

'It was difficult to tell,' writes Mr Spicer, 'owing to the winding road. To begin with, the funnel had the appearance of a fairly broad cone, tapering down towards the ground from the general cloud base, but five or so minutes later it had narrowed considerably and was clear of the ground.' By the time he reached the junction with the A4538 near Sneachill it had decayed into a narrow rope of cloud but was more or less overhead. From the time he first saw it to this point was about 15 minutes.

The weather that day was mostly overcast with cumulus clouds of all shapes and sizes. The tornado seemed to be associated with an intense but very localised shower and a black cloud that arrived shortly after, so rapid convection would probably explain it. There did not seem to be any thunder or lightning, so far as it was possible to judge from inside a moving car.

'I have no idea whether this whirlwind touched down or caused anyone any injury, or even damage to buildings. Nor was there any mention of it in the news. I learned years later that a photograph had been taken of it but I have not been able to find out who took it,' says Mr Spicer. He adds that his weather notes show only a low moving northwards over the Midlands at that time.

11th August 1985:
Whirlwind Strikes Girl Guide Camp

On 11th August an International Girl Guide Camp was being held at the Three Counties showground in Malvern. Suddenly, out of nowhere came a 40 mph gale which seemed to sweep down from the hills with great force. A vigorous low pressure

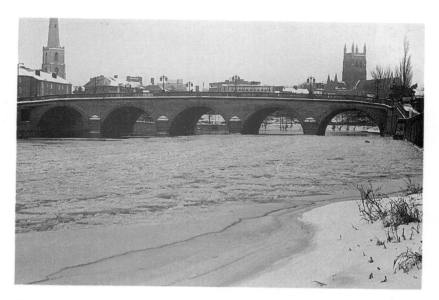

The frozen river Severn at Worcester, 1987.

area had funnelled a zone of squally winds into the area, with devastating results.

With trees in full summer foliage the force of the wind blew more than 100 down and stripped branches from others. What appeared to be a mini-whirlwind ripped through that part of Malvern. Wind speeds were recorded at 65 mph, the strongest summer winds logged since records began in the area.

VIP visitors touring the camp, including Police Chief Superintendent Mike Read and local councillor Martin Hudson, had to hang on to one marquee to prevent it being blown away. No one was hurt but a video screen was damaged and Worcester Guides Christine Vaughan and Elizabeth Pearman, both 14 years of age, reported that some of the leaders' tents and the toilets were blown down.

A bird's eye view of the flood plain at Worcester in 1988.

The whirlwind picked up debris, branches and bins, cartwheeling them down the roads. The wind storm grabbed everything in its path and nearby electricity lines were reported as cracking and sparking as the lines touched in the twisting wind. The same wind moved northwards, striking Stourport-on-Severn. Small boats on a countryside lake were overturned, mature trees uprooted and tiles and slates sent flying through the air. Large panes of glass from houses and glasshouses were hurled 20 ft in the air.

It was, and is still considered to be, the worst summer windstorm recorded in the area.

7th May 1988: The Sahara Comes To England

On several occasions in the past the right meteorological pattern has prevailed to bring a coating of red sand from the Sahara to the county. On 7th May many awoke to find sand-coated windscreens, glasshouses and windows.

A spell of south to south-easterly winds brought air northwards from the desert across North Africa. Sand was transported in the upper air currents after being whipped up by the strong squally winds over the Sahara, and deposited over central and southern England, with Herefordshire and Worcestershire catching their fair share. As it encountered rain-bearing cloud it was washed

Water, water, everywhere. Wet-suited Malcolm Hodgetts at deep mid-wicket at Worcester cricket ground during early January 1988.

out of the atmosphere by Mother Nature, leaving the sand behind once the rain had evaporated away.

Worcester Weather Centre was inundated with calls from anxious car owners trying to find out where the deposit came from and what it was. The sand, browny-red coloured, covered many surfaces and this occurrence was considered even more widespread than the fall in May 1968.

INTO THE NINETIES

1st February 1990: Counting The Cost

Gales affected Worcestershire between 3.30 pm and 6.30 pm, with wind speeds higher than 50 mph. Herefordshire suffered the most, automatic weather stations logging gusts of up to 75 and 80 mph during this brief period.

The high winds brought damage and destruction to the area, with businesses and homes thrown into chaos as the storm reached its peak. Trees came crashing down and caused a great deal of structural damage. Over £30,000 worth of damage was done to Yeoman's Canyon Travel bus garage at Three Elms near Hereford. At Aylestone Hill a massive cedar tree, said to be over 150 years old, succumbed to the hurricane-force winds just after 2 pm and the road had to be closed off. A caravan caught by the tree was crumpled like paper and the debris scattered over a wide area. A tree also came down in Roman Road, and dangerous chimneys had to be dealt with by the fire brigade in Union Street, Dawes Road, Bridge Street and Ledbury Road. Falling slates and television aerials added to the damage, and gardens were devastated.

Insurance companies were hit hard as claims began to mount following the swathe of damage across the Herefordshire countryside. The Royal Insurance Company, based in Widemarsh Street in Hereford, gave the green light to policy holders with

Part of the damage at the Three Elms' bus garage after the hurricane-force winds of February 1990.

A large cedar tree crashed down across the main Hereford to Worcester road at Aylestone Hill during the gales of January 1990.

insurance claims to go ahead up to £2,000 without estimates, though claims over that amount still had to go through the normal procedures.

February 1990: Nice Weather For Ducks

From 1st to 15th February winds and heavy rain lashed this picturesque part of the county. 'Storm force winds proved the undoing of the medieval weather cock on top of St Peter's church at Peterchurch, leaving it looking very sorry for itself,' wrote Veronica Gooley of the *Herefordshire Times*.

People found their journeys home from work taking two hours or more as the flood chaos worsened. At 11.30 pm on the Thursday, *Herefordshire Times* photographer Derek Foster and

She found the best way to travel across St Martins Street, Hereford in early February 1990!

Edgar Street, Hereford under flood water in February 1990.

The (Evening) News must get through — we would like to tell you something you already know!

his wife Doreen hit trouble at Rotherwas. They had taken the back road to Hereford because of landslides and fallen trees at Mordiford, and their car was suddenly engulfed by flood water. The water covered the headlights, cut out the engine and the car began floating. Luckily, they were rescued by a policeman who was checking a house nearby, and were driven home safely to Tupsley.

The Wye reached 16 ft 2 inches, compared with 16 ft 8 inches in 1981, 17 ft 4 inches in 1979 and 20 ft in 1960. The floods did bring some fringe benefits. Thirty swans and their cygnets left the river for the calmer waters of the Lugg Meadows, along with wading and water birds of all kinds, and hours of enjoyment were had by birdwatchers. It was reported that some people even indulged in windsurfing on the meadow.

19th April 1990: The Day Crabs Fell

This Thursday turned out to be a typical April day with a mixture of bright sunny intervals and frequent showers, funnelling down the Cheshire Gap into the county. The showers were heavy and squally with hail. They fell from large cumulus and cumulonimbus clouds, which have strong up and down draughts and are often accompanied by hail and thunder.

By evening the showers were merging into longer spells of rain, and around nine o'clock a sudden squall swept in across both counties. The anemometer reading here in Worcester peaked at 62 mph and as the squall line passed through heavy hail began to rattle the windowpanes. Half an inch in diameter, the hail soon coated the ground with a white layer resembling a snow shower.

At the end of the squall at 9.30 pm I took my weather observations, but while walking across the large lawned area I noticed a movement that I took to be worms. On closer inspection, it turned out to be small crabs.

The tote office on the racecourse at Pitchcroft, Worcester, wrecked by high winds in February 1990.

The large cumulonimbus cloud which had built up over the sea near North Wales had sucked up these small creatures, transported them to our area and deposited them in various parts of the county. I gathered as many as possible and took them down to the river Severn to give them a chance of survival.

May 1990: Dust Devils

With less than half an inch of rain in the area during this month it turned out to be one of the driest since our records began more than 25 years ago. Some very hot days were logged and the month had record sightings of dust devils and whirlwinds, these occurring on those hot days when the ground heated up rapidly. The average long term air temperature is 16.1°C (61°F), but during this month the daily average maximum was logged in well above at just over 20.3°C (68°F), the top temperature being recorded early on in that famous month on Thursday 3rd May at 28.6°C (83°F). And it was on this day that no fewer than ten dust devils were spotted and reported in.

The ground turned hot by mid afternoon, making it very uneven temperature-wise. It created sudden surges upwards of columns of hot air, with the cooler upper air rushing downwards to take its place and encouraging the air to swirl and twist.

About four in the afternoon, out of a clear Mediterranean-blue sky, I noticed a dark vortex rising about one mile upwards, two miles or so away to the west of my weather centre. Paper, dust, leaves and debris were twisting around within it at tremendous speed. The wind flow was easterly but it was travelling against the prevailing wind direction. I watched it for at least ten minutes before it disintegrated and vanished from sight.

By about teatime of that day ten reports had been logged. The one not far from the station had been spotted and observed by a Mrs Evans of Hallow. She reported that the wind had arisen out of nowhere during a calm sunny spell. Dustbin lids were lifted high into the sky, dust and debris were pulled upwards, and her patio set was knocked over and the umbrella sucked up. The wind created such a roar that it resembled a train or heavy lorry passing by, though as it headed away it seemed to hiss like a snake. She had never experienced anything like it before in her life, 'it was most frightening due to its noise and suddenness'.

Summer 1990: A Spell Of Great Heat

From 30th July to 4th August 1990 soaring temperatures brought record sales of ice cream, soft drinks, sunwear and sun lotions. The media weighed in with headlines such as 'Britain Scorches' and 'Phew, What A Scorcher!'

Our station here in Worcester was often mentioned in the 'Met Section' of newspapers worldwide as being the hot spot of Britain. On 2nd August we peaked at a temperature of 36.6°C (98°F), the hottest in the country, and when it became clear that we could hit 38°C (100°F) the next day, radio and television crews and reporters from several national newspapers sped to the station to record this unusual event as it happened.

With television cameras poised to catch the memorable moment on film — and crews poised to speed the video tape back to their studios to be used at teatime — the mercury in the thermometer hit the sweltering, dizzy height of 37°C (99°F). Out came the soft drinks to cool everyone down, while I posed with a pink-swimsuit-clad young model drinking wine by the thermometer screen. This reading was the highest recorded since our logbooks began, and the spell has been called the Great Heat of 1990.

23rd September 1990: Hail The Size Of Golf Balls

After a showery morning with a squally north to north-west wind blowing, a cluster of thunderstorms visited first Herefordshire and then Worcestershire between 3 pm and 6.30 pm. The wind was said to have picked up three henhouses close to Hay-on-Wye, destroying them and scattering the birds in terror.

During that same storm came a sudden squall, and Mr White of Ludlow spotted a glow in the sky which turned out to be a thunderbolt. It hit a nearby tree, destroying it instantly. Hail of a size never before seen in that area also fell, the ice balls about two or three inches in circumference. It stripped foliage from trees, damaged glasshouses and frames, and caused some injuries. Two horses were killed in the storm, which was extremely localised.

January 1991: Flashes In The Sky

A day of gusty winds and driving rains caused some localised flooding on 5th January. As the winds increased through the

Structural damage to a block of flats near Hereford after the hurricane force winds of 6th January 1991.

evening, automatic weather stations in the county logged wind speeds gusting to 60 mph by 9 pm, with gusts to 79 mph in south-west Herefordshire. The wind affected electric cables, sending out flashes into the night sky as the cables touched.

During the early hours of 6th January, the wind gusted to 75 mph in Worcestershire and to 85 mph, hurricane force, in Herefordshire. Trees were brought down in great numbers and structural damage was widespread. A whirlwind affected the area south of Ross-on-Wye with two garden sheds brought to the ground, and a wall came crashing down near Ludlow. The sky was frequently alight with electric charges from cables, and many people phoned in to the station mistaking the flashes as a gathering thunderstorm. By the morning the winds slowly abated.

27th January 1991: Shiver And Slide

A weather front brought sleet, snow and drizzle into the county on 27th January. Early that morning with air temperatures around zero and the ground surface temperature below that by 2°, the drizzle froze. It encased the branches of trees and shrubs and formed glaze ice on roads and pavements. Numerous cars 'bumped' on county roads as the ice built up.

The noise of the freezing drizzle falling resembled an eerie cracking, popping sound, bringing people from their beds to find out the cause. The station received many calls during that early morning period. The county shivered and cars slid about well into the morning.

7th & 8th February 1991: Blizzard Chaos

Bitterly cold east to south-east winds from off a very cold Continent plunged Herefordshire and Worcestershire into winter. Snow flurries in the morning turned to more continuous light snow through the afternoon, producing a dusting of white on the ground. Air temperatures remained very low all day with the thermometer reading −5.6°C (22°F) with severe wind chill.

After midnight the snow became heavy, whipped by a strong wind. By morning the countryside had been turned into a white wonderland. The snow blizzards continued through the day on the 8th, with more frost to follow on that night. Six inches of level snow was logged from that blizzard, but considerable drifting occurred giving piles of snow 10 ft deep in rural areas and creating havoc on roads. Some villages were completely cut off.

Icicles 5 ft long and 6 inches in circumference, with sharp pointed ends, were hanging from the viaduct in Croft Road in Worcester.

Fun in the snow at the Winder house in Worcester in February 1991.

December 1991: Cider Snow

The *Herefordshire Times* reported on 12th December that parts of the county had experienced their own exclusive snow storm the day before. One theory put forward for this strange occurrence was that it was caused by 'cider flakes'.

People in the Whitecross, Moorfields, Belmont Road and Broomy Hill areas awoke to find fine snow falling and donned wellington boots to walk to work. But they soon felt frauds when they arrived in a snow-free city centre. A spokesman at the meteorological office in Bristol said the private snowstorm could have been caused by a number of contributory factors – the freezing fog, a temperature of $-7°C$, the dampness of the area and the condensation of vapour emitted into the air.

David Speakman and his son Thomas, with the remains of the tree hit by a lightning bolt in May 1992.

It was possible that the latter was caused by cider-maker H.P. Bulmer's chimney at Moorfields, which gives off totally harmless water vapour from the apple drying line. Hence, 'cider snow'.

Earth Tremors

There have been two earth tremors in the Herefordshire and Worcestershire area in the 1990s, and six others are recorded since 1850.

9th November 1852: At 4.15 am a violent tremor shook the area. Livestock were said to have been restless and troubled at least 24 hours ahead of the shockwave. Some damage was reported and many items were moved and broken.

Racegoers lose out again — more canoe practice, this time at Pitchcroft, just after Christmas, 1993.

Physician heal thyself! A family firm of builders, at Lyde near Hereford, suffered extensive damage to their roof after a lightning strike in early June, 1994.

6th October 1852: The earth shook for many seconds, bringing damage and terror to country communities as household objects moved and fell from walls and shelves.

1896: A severe earth tremor affected the whole area with damage caused to buildings. Some livestock were reported to be affected to the point they had to be put down. Large cracks appeared in walls and on the clay ground.

15th August 1926: A shock affected many parts. The Tintern Walking Tour was on at the time and many walkers felt the shockwaves. Cattle were seen in a disturbed state in the meadows. The tremor lasted about 30 seconds.

11th February 1957: A small tremor occurred at 3.45 pm. In comparison with past tremors, this lasted just a second or two and was logged as a very minor one.

19th July 1984: At 7.55 am the earth shook. The tremor was logged as 4 on the Richter Scale with the Worcester Weather Centre receiving many calls from concerned people. Walls were cracked, chinaware broken, pictures moved on walls and people who were in tall buildings felt strong movements from side to side.

2nd April 1990: A tremor which struck at 2.47 pm was considered to be the worst in living memory. It measured 5.2 on the Richter Scale. Damage was noticeable and some people reported hearing a hissing sound just before it struck.

12th May 1994: Many people were awakened from sleep by a strong tremor which shook a large part of the area, measuring 3 on the Richter Scale. No damage was reported, but objects and pictures moved and houses shook for a few seconds. The epicentre of the tremor was situated close by Cleeve Prior at 2 am.

Glossary Of Common Weather Terms

Altitude: Height above sea level.

Anticyclone: An area of high pressure bringing settled weather, but it can bring on frost and fog during autumn, winter or spring.

Atmosphere: The gaseous envelope surrounding the earth.

Ball lightning: A suspended sphere of radiating energy. A slow-burning admixture of air and carbon or an ionised mass of gas.

Barometer: An instrument for the measurement of atmospheric pressure.

Clouds: Water vapour which has condensed. See below for cloud classification.

Cloudy: A cloudy day is one where the total cloud covers or nearly covers the entire sky.

Col: The slack pressure between two highs and two lows.

Cold front: The division between a warm air mass and a cold air mass, it brings heavy squalls and hail and thunder.

Depression or Low: A mass of ascending air accompanied by cloud and rain or snow with often strong winds, especially in winter.

Drought: A prolonged period without precipitation. Usually an official drought can be declared after 15 consecutive days with rainfall no more than 0.01 inches (0.2mm).

Fog: May come from radiation cooling the ground, or move in on the back of a wind (advection fog), or form when warm air runs over cold ground (as during a rapid thaw).

Frost: Forms when skies are clear overnight and the wind falls calm. Vales or hollows will be most at risk from frost. When the ground temperature falls below freezing it is called a ground frost and when the air temperature falls below 0°C (32°F) it is then called an air frost.

Gale: A gale is defined as a surface wind of mean speed of 34 knots or more averaged over a period of ten minutes.

Glaze ice: Rain which instantly freezes on contact with the ground causing dangerous conditions both under foot and on roads.

Gust: A rapid increase in strength of the wind relative to the mean strength at the time.

Hail: Precipitation which has frozen into particles of ice which vary in size. Layers of ice build one on another as it is suspended in the violent up-draughts of cumulonimbus clouds until they become heavy enough to overcome the turbulent currents and fall to the surface as hail.

Hurricane: Stormy winds in excess of 64 knots or 73 mph; usually occurs within the tropical climes of the world and feeds off very warm seas.

Lightning: The energy released and produced by an electrical discharge within the clouds or from between clouds and the ground.

Rain: Liquid precipitation, the individual droplets measuring up to 6mm (0.24 inches) in diameter.

Rainbow: Optical phenomena occurring when sunlight is refracted into spectral colours by rain falling from shower clouds. The larger the raindrops, the more intense the rainbow.

Ridge of High Pressure: A region or extension of a high, where air is subsiding.

Showers: They mostly occur within unstable air of Maritime Polar Air. Heaped cumulus and cumulonimbus clouds form after a clear sunny start, they expand and become larger in size and showers most frequently break out between late morning and early evening. On showery days the nights are often clear and starry.

Sleet: Precipitation consisting of a mixture of melting snow and rain.

Snow: Precipitation which falls as frozen flakes in the shape of six-pointed stars.

Stratosphere: The region of the upper atmosphere above the tropopause. No weather is found there.

Thermometer: An instrument for measuring the temperature.

Thunder: The sound produced by the air becoming heated at great temperatures. It heats up and expands at great speed, creating the sound waves we hear as thunder.

Thunderstorm: A rapid ascent of warm moist air usually associated with cumulonimbus development. Raindrops turn to ice in the anvil-shaped top of the cloud giving a positive charge, and are split by the up-draughts of the storm cloud near its bottom creating a negative build up, with a positive charge running through everything on the ground beneath the cloud. This produces lightning discharges and the sound we call thunder, with hail, rain and squalls all likely.

Tornado: A violent spiral of wind, travelling at tremendous speeds, tornadoes may create severe damage and some loss of life where they occur.

Tropopause: Region of the atmosphere above eight miles up which puts a lid on weather processes by preventing any further ascent of air from the troposphere. It is characterised by temperature remaining constant with height.

Troposphere: The region of the atmosphere in which weather processes occur, with the temperature falling off with height.

Trough: A region or an extension of a low pressure where the air is mainly ascending, producing rain or showers.

Warm Front: The division between cool or cold air and warm or milder air. The warm front is where warm air meets the earth's surface; it is the air behind the front which gives it its name.

Wind: The process of pressure equalisation, air being moved from high pressure to low pressure areas.

Cloud Classifications

Altocumulus (Ac): White, grey patches or layers, rounded masses or rolls. Height of base 6,500 ft to 23,000 ft.

Altostratus (As): Blue-grey layer thick enough to hide the sun, very uniform. Height of base 6,500 ft to 23,000 ft.

Cirrocumulus (Cc): Thin white patches or sheets, resembling grains, ripples or waves. Height of base 16,500 to 45,000 ft.

Cirrostratus (Cs): Transparent white cloud veil, very milky and creates halo. Height of base 16,500 ft to 45,000 ft.

Cirrus (Ci): Fibrous, hair-like appearance. Height of base 16,500 ft to 45,000 ft.

Cumulonimbus (Cb): Heavy dense vertical clouds with anvil-shaped tops. The anvil top is smooth, fibrous or striated and is nearly always flat. Beneath the base the cloud is black or very dark. Hail, thunder, squalls and rain storms accompany these storm clouds. Height of base 1,500 ft to 6,500 ft.

Cumulus (Cu): Detached heaped clouds, in the form of rising domes or towers. Brilliant white cauliflower shapes, with dark bases towards the horizon. Height of base 1,500 ft to 6,500 ft.

Nimbostratus (Ns): Grey cloud layer, appearing diffused due to falling rain. Lower ragged patches occur below. Height of base 3,000 ft to 10,000 ft.

Stratocumulus (Sc): Grey or whitish sheet with dark parts. Rounded masses or rolls which sometimes merge together. Height of base 1,500 ft to 6,500 ft.

Stratus (St): White-grey layer; rain, drizzle or slight snow may fall from it. Sometimes it forms ragged patches. Height of base surface to 1,500 ft.

Acknowledgements

The author would like to thank the following companies and individuals for their help with the photographs and other illustrations in this book: – the archive staffs of Worcester Evening News and Reed Midland Newspapers Ltd., the Hereford Times group, Mike Grundy, Mr A Bryan, Derek Foster, Madge Hooper, Peter Ainsley, Brian Peplow, Ann Powell, George Jeynes, Mrs E Barwell, Mrs Tudge, Roly Jenkins, Roger Hooper.

Finally, many thanks to the countless other professional and amateur weather observers for their help and enthusiasm, without whom this book would not have been possible.

Paul Damari

Index